The COACHING Workshop

For Christian Leaders

Participant Manual

The COACHING Workshop
For Christian Leaders

Powerful Leadership Skills for Solving Problems,
Reaching Goals, & Developing Others

Participant Manual

Keith E. Webb

Creative Results Management

Creative Results Management
www.creativeresultsmanagement.com

The COACHING Workshop for Christian Leaders

ISBN-13: 978-1-944000-02-8

Version 3.0

Cover design by Kyle Walling.

Notice to Participant

Table of Contents

Workshop Overview & Objectives

When you complete this workshop, you will be able to:

- Evaluate and determine personal development needs.
- Review and practice core coaching skills of Listening Actively, Asking Powerful Questions, Generating Feedback, Designing Actions, and Following Up.
- Combine coaching skills and practice using The COACH Model®.
- Formulate next steps for continued learning and skill development.

Ground Rules

These are some basic "ground rules" or group norms that we will function with during this program. Space at the end is for additions from the group.

- What's said here stays here
- Phones off – receive/send messages on breaks
- We're all learners
- Participate fully
- Arrive and leave on time (We'll stop and start on time)
- Okay to move around as needed
- Work hard and have fun!

Other Ground Rules

-
-
-
-

What I Want to Learn

I'd like greater knowledge and understanding of the following:

Example: I'd like to know a simple model for helping people make good decisions.

_____

_____

_____

_____

_____

I'd like greater skills in doing the following:

Example: I'd like to be able to ask more powerful questions.

_____

_____

_____

_____

_____

I'd like to further clarify or explore the following attitudes, feelings, and preferences:

Example: I'd like to really value what people say.

_____

_____

_____

_____

Introduction to Coaching

The purposes of a person's heart are deep waters, but one who has insight draws them out.

—Proverbs 20:5

Coaching isn't about teaching people what you know. It's about helping them learn.

—Keith Webb

The illiterate of the 21st century will not be those who cannot read and write, but those who cannot learn, unlearn, and relearn.

—Alvin Toffler

Mankind's search for meaning is the primary motivation in his life and not a secondary rationalization of instinctual drives.

—Viktor Frankl

Integrating Coaching Skills into Other Roles

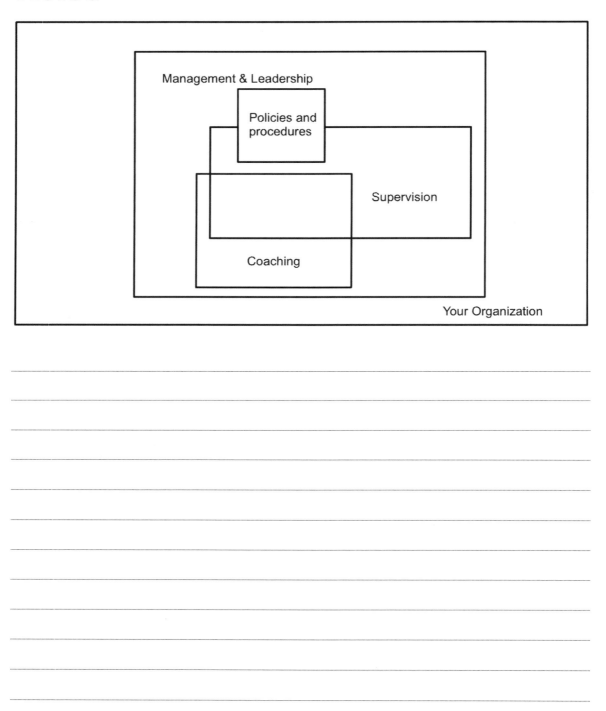

Asking vs. Telling

In many societies, the act of leading is equated with telling, being directive, and having the answers. "Telling" is only one way to lead, with a number of disadvantages. Coaching is based on asking and drawing out of the other person, having many advantages. Let's compare…

Disadvantages of Telling

Advantages of Asking

Keith Webb's Story

Definition of Coaching

Coaching Assumptions

> But the Counselor, the Holy Spirit, whom the Father will send in my name,
>
> will teach you all things and will remind you of everything I have said to
>
> you.
>
> —John 14:26

1. The Holy Spirit speaks to people directly through many means. He is the best source for insights, ideas, strategies, and action points. Coaches help the coachee to hear the Holy Spirit more clearly and support them to respond well.

2. All people have a holistic calling – being and doing – and may need additional clarity and growth in one or more aspects of their calling.

3. Coachee-generated insights, ideas, strategies, and action points are most relevant and useful to the coachee who immediately owns them.

4. By using special communication techniques, tools, and models, coaches can significantly speed up and improve the quality of the coachee's insights, ideas, strategies, and action points.

Spiritual Dynamics in Coaching

The Holy Spirit

> But the Counselor, the Holy Spirit, whom the Father will send in my name,
>
> will teach you all things and will remind you of everything I have said to
>
> you.   —John 14:26

All Christians have the Holy Spirit inside. Jesus sent believers a Counselor (John 14:15-18) to teach and remind (John 14:26).

Christian coaches are not a substitute for the Holy Spirit. Sometimes we forget this. Experience, intuition, and spiritual discernment can tempt coaches to move to conclusions. More important than the coach's perspective is the Holy Spirit's perspective and how He's leading the coachee.

All believers have the Holy Spirit, but not all believers hear His voice and know how to respond well. Listening to the Holy Spirit is key to understanding God's will.

The coach's job is to provoke reflection in the coachee, toward the Holy Spirit. A good coach draws out what the Holy Spirit has put in.

How much do you trust the Holy Spirit to "teach and remind"?

The Body of Christ

Every believer has the Holy Spirit and thus a direct link to God without a human priest mediator. Spiritual discernment is a social, not individualistic, process. God created the Body of Christ as a social setting where His will is made known, interpreted, and applied. A person outside an active role in the Body of Christ cannot fully understand and apply God's will in his or her life.

Consider the relational nature of humans:

> *Persona* in Latin comes from the Greek word *prosopon*, which can be translated "face to face." Each human is a person as he or she stands face to face, turned toward another person, engaged in dialogue, involved in relationship. We discover our personhood in community, in relationship.
>
> —Anderson & Reese, in *Spiritual Mentoring*

The Christian coach plays an important role in helping coachees to think through how they are processing their spiritual discernment with others and how they might involve the appropriate members of the Body of Christ in that process. Coachees mature through their interaction with the Body of Christ.

Find and Join God's Work in the Coachee

A basic, and Biblical, assumption of the Christian coach is that God is already at work in the life of the coachee.

> In his defense Jesus said to them, 'My Father is always at his work to this very day, and I too am working.' 'Very truly I tell you, the Son can do nothing by himself; he can do only what he sees his Father doing, …'.
>
> —John 5:17, 19b

If Jesus could do nothing by himself, then how much more should we abandon our agendas, strategies, and plans for the coachee and instead join the Father in His work in and through the coachee? He will continue to work in the coachee, with or without us.

> …being confident of this, he who began a good work in you will carry it on to completion until the day of Christ Jesus.
>
> —Philippians 1:6

The key to effective coaching is for coachee and coach to understand what God is doing and join His work.

The Transformational Formula

There are four key elements that facilitate transformation:

1. Holy Spirit
2. Discovery
3. Action
4. Reinforcement

Each is essential to the transformational formula. Transformation rarely happens without all four. Just for fun, let's write it as a formula:

$$T = (D + A + R)^{HS}$$

Transformation is the result of the sum of discovery (D), action (A), and reinforcement (R), raised to the power of the Holy Spirit.

Discovery

The coaching process is focused on discovery. Discovery comes in the form of new self-awareness, insights, ideas, learning, attitudes, facts, realizations, etc. The bread and butter of coaching are discovery and action.

Action

Without action steps coaching is merely a nice conversation. Although encouraging, without action there is no change, no translation of any new discoveries into the life of the coachee. Coaching is about action.

Reinforcement

As coachees act on their discoveries they get some kind of feedback—a result, a reward, or consequence. This feedback can reinforce or weaken the new behavior of the coachee. The coach must reinforce all actions taken toward the coachee's desired ends, regardless of the actual results.

Holy Spirit

The Holy Spirit is the ultimate generator of discovery and action. It is the Holy Spirit who brings transformation to the lives of people. The reinforcement of the Holy Spirit through peace, fulfillment, and a lack of panging conscience encourage a person to further transformation.

Notes

Listening Actively

My dear brothers and sisters, take note of this: everyone should be quick to listen, slow to speak and slow to become angry,...Those who consider themselves religious and yet do not keep a tight rein on their tongues deceive themselves, and their religion is worthless.

—James 1:19; 26

If you think you know, you're not fully listening.

—Keith Webb

Being heard is so close to being loved that for the average person, they are almost indistinguishable.

—David W. Augsburger

Who speaks, sows; who listens, reaps.

—Argentine Proverb

Discussion on Listening

How do you know when someone isn't listening to you well?

_____

_____

_____

How does it make you feel?

_____

_____

_____

What do you appreciate about someone listening to you?

_____

_____

_____

The 80/20 Rule

In coaching, the focus of the conversation is on the coachee. They set the agenda, they talk the most, and they create their own action plans. The coachee talks and the coach listens 80% of the time. Listening is of great value to the coachee and a wonderful gift to give.

Listening Principle: If you are talking, you are not listening.

— Steve Ogne

Notes

How to Listen Better

Listening is a skill. You can learn how to listen better. There are many ways to do this, as you will learn in this section.

1. Listen with your mind

- Give the coachee your attention.
- Try to enter into their frame of reference, their world.
- Focus on what's behind their words.
- Don't let your mind wander.
-
-

2. Listen with your body

- Sound interested.
- Do you have the proper amount of eye contact?
- Let your arms, hands, and body posture say, "I'm interested."
- Your non-verbal will be "seen" even over the telephone.
- What are the coachee's non-verbal signals communicating to you?
- Check your assumptions about the non-verbal with the coachee.
-
-

3. Listen with your words

- Ask clarifying questions.
- Don't finish sentences or provide missing words.
- Don't give advice or solutions while they are talking.
- Summarize main points.
- WAIT: Why Am I Talking?
-
-

4. Listen with your intuition

- Listen for the meaning behind the words, gestures, and body language.
- What is the coachee *not* saying?
- Test your intuition with clarifying questions.
-
-

5. Listen with the Holy Spirit

- Use spiritual discernment.
- If you hear from the Holy Spirit, then ask, Should I share this with the coachee? And When should I communicate this?
- How can you share this in a way to enable the discovery process?
-
-

Thinking About it...

Clarifying Questions

Use clarifying questions to improve your listening and understanding. Sometimes we *think* we understand what the person is saying, but they mean something different.

And this is not just for your understanding. By asking a person to clarify, they explain more fully. In doing so they often reveal meaning. This allows them to gain awareness and for you to "coach the person" more easily.

Clarifying Meaning

What do you mean by ...? ("significant contribution")

Could you give an example of ...? ("being on top of things")

What does ... mean to you? ("more responsibility")

Clarifying Desires

What would it look like if you were ...? ("a better manager")

What would you do differently if you were...? ("more intentional")

Clarifying Thought Processes

What makes you say that?

What leads you to that conclusion?

Clarifying Being

What is happening inside you as you talk about this?

What are your thoughts on what you've said so far?

The COACH Model®

I pray that the eyes of your heart may be enlightened in order that you may know the hope to which he has called you, the riches of his glorious inheritance in his holy people, and his incomparably great power for us who believe.

—Ephesians 1:18-19a

Your ability to get things done, make changes, or help other people grow depends on the quality of your conversations.

—Keith Webb

You cannot teach a person anything. You can only help them discover it within themselves.

—Galileo Galilei

I am always ready to learn although I do not always like being taught.

—Winston Churchill

The COACH Model®

Following a simple coaching model will help you to coach better. The COACH Model® has five steps to guide you through a coaching conversation.

Connect: Engage

The first step is to connect with the coachee and build rapport and trust. It's a human connection between coach and coachee. And it's a spiritual connection between the Holy Spirit and coachee & coach. Over time, the implementation of this step will change as the relationship grows.

Example Questions:

How have you been?

What insights have you had since our last conversation?

What has God been doing in your life lately?

A coach will also use this time to **follow-up** the last conversation's action steps. Example Questions:

What progress did you make on your action steps?

Outcome: Determine Conversation Goal

Find out what the coachee considers to be a valuable topic for the coaching conversation. Through dialogue, the coach and coachee determine how to best use the coaching conversation. This may mean continuing previous topics or engaging in new ones.

Example Questions:

Where would you like to focus our conversation?

What makes this important for you right now?

What result would you like to take away from our conversation?

Awareness: Reflective Dialogue

Ask questions and practice active listening. Listen beyond the coachee's words. Encourage and give feedback appropriately. Challenge assumptions appropriately. Encourage discovery, insights, commitment, and action through a reflective dialogue. **Discovery** is the key to this stage.

Example Questions:

What are the key issues to address?

What are you learning about yourself (or the situation) as we talk?

How are we doing at getting to the result you wanted?

What would you like to explore next?

Practice all the coaching skills seeking discovery and follow up with questions like these:

What else do you think or feel about this?

What would help you move forward?

Course: Action Steps

This step seeks to capture the insights and put them into actionable steps. Coach and coachee will continue a reflective dialogue, but this time focused towards a course of action. The result will be clear action steps the coachee will do before the next coaching conversation. Try for 2-3 action steps for each coaching topic.

Example Questions:

> **What actions could you take to move forward?**

> **How confident are you that you can do this?** (If not confident, work on the plan.)

> **What support do you need?**

> **Which of these will you commit to doing?**

Highlights: Learning & Action Steps

Ask the coachee to reflect on their learning, insights, and what they found helpful. This review helps the coachee to deepen their learning, and helps the coach know what the coachee found valuable.

Example Questions:

> **What awareness do you have now that you didn't before?**

> **What makes this significant for you?**

Determining the Conversation Outcome

Do two walk together unless they have agreed to do so?   —Amos 3:3

The topics of coaching conversations usually come from the coachee. There are three steps to creating a helpful Outcome: 1) identify the topic, 2) exploring why it's important, and 3) creating a measure of success.

Example:

Coach: Where would you like to focus our conversation?

Coachee: I want to grow in my relationship with my spouse.

Coach: What part of this would you like to talk about to move you forward this week?

Coachee: I want the relationship we had when we were first married.

Coach: What's an example of that kind of relationship?

Coachee: Sure. Everything was new and fresh. We had time for each other, and it was exciting just to be together. It just doesn't feel like that anymore. It seems like everything we do is focused on the kids or doing work around the house.

Coach: What makes this important to you right now?

Coachee: I feel like we're drifting apart, and don't like it.

Coach: What does "moving together" rather than "drifting apart" look like?

Coachee: We would be together. Not just physically, but mentally present. We'd be growing more internally connected, at a heart level. Right now, we're just dividing up the tasks of running our family.

Coach: What result would you like to take away from our conversation?

Coachee: "I want time together with my spouse that's focused on just us."

Coach: What specifically would you like to have by the end of our conversation?

Coachee: I would like to create a plan to help us regularly connect in heart and mind.

Adding F.I.R.E. To Your Conversations

Focus

Ask the coachee what they want as the focus of the conversation.

> **Where would you like to focus our conversation?**

> **What would be most helpful for us to work on?**

Importance

Use questions to explore, clarify, and focus the coachee's topic / problem / goal. This step can be the source of much discovery and relief for an overwhelmed coachee.

> **What makes that important for you?**

> **What would achieving that do for you? For others?**

> **What's the bigger issue behind this situation?**

Result

After exploring the topic, ask the coachee to say what specific result he or she wants.

> **What result would you like to take away from our conversation?**

> **What do you hope to have settled by the end of our conversation?**

Evaluate

Midway through the coaching conversation, check in (evaluate) the progress toward the coachee's desired result.

> **How are we doing at getting to the result you wanted?**

> **Are we on track, how would you like to proceed?**

Other Questions to Stoke the Outcome F.I.R.E.

Narrowing questions

That's a big topic, what part of that would you like to focus on today?

What aspect of that problem would you like to work on right now?

What part of this would be most immediately helpful to you to address this week?

Clarifying questions

What do you mean by _____ ?

Could you give an example of _____ ?

What would _____ look like if you could become that?

Confirming Questions

Just so we're clear, would you please restate what you'd like to work on today?

Today you'd like to work on _____ . Is that right?

Is that what you'd like to focus our conversation on today?

Jesus: "What do you want?"

Three times the Gospels record Jesus asking people what they want. Amazing. He has so much to offer, so much insight to their real needs, yet He allows these people to lead the conversation according to how they perceive their own needs or interests. What do you notice in these conversations?

James and John's Mother

> Then the mother of Zebedee's sons came to Jesus with her sons and, kneeling down, asked a favor of him. 'What is it you want?' he asked. She said, 'Grant that one of these two sons of mine may sit at your right and the other at your left in your kingdom.' 'You don't know what you are asking,' Jesus said to them.   —Matthew 20:20-22a

Two Blind Men

> Jesus stopped and called them, 'What do you want me to do for you?' he asked. 'Lord,' they answered, 'we want our sight.' Jesus had compassion on them and touched their eyes. Immediately they received their sight and followed him.   —Matthew 20:32-34

Andrew and Another Disciple

> …Jesus saw them following and asked, 'what do you want?' They said, 'Rabbi' (which means 'Teacher'), 'where are you staying?' 'Come,' he replied, 'and you will see.' So they went and saw where he was staying, and spent that day with him.   —John 1:38-39a

Asking Powerful Questions

After three days they found him in the temple courts, sitting among the teachers, listening to them and asking them questions. Everyone who heard him was amazed at his understanding and his answers.

—Luke 2:46-47

The power of coaching isn't in providing answers, but in asking thought-provoking questions.

—Keith Webb

Change begins the moment you ask the question.

—Cooperrider, Whiney, & Stavros

Open questions are the single sure practice that invites critical thinking and effective learning.

—Jane Vella

Asking Powerful Questions

> The purposes of a person's heart are deep waters, but one who has
>
> insight draws them out.   —Proverbs 20:5

Powerful Questions

Powerful questions come from profound listening and engagement with a person. What makes a question powerful is its ability to provoke reflection in the other person.

1. Coachee or Me?
   Is this question for my benefit or the coachee's?

2. Forward or Backward?
   Is this question focused on the past or moving forward?

3. Exploring or Correcting?
   Does this question try to correct the coachee or help him or her explore?

Towards Powerful Questions

Compare the amount of reflection the following questions will likely generate.

1. Are you happy with your work?
2. How do you feel about your work?
3. What about your work do you find most satisfying?
4. How does your work connect to your calling?

My Idea → Open Questions

In the questions below, the coach's ideas are leaking into the conversation. To generate better reflection, ask more open, broad questions by beginning with What, How, When, Where, & Who.

Example:

Closed: Are you planning to <u>borrow</u> the money to do that?

Open: What are your plans to <u>pay for</u> that?

Questions to Open Up	Initials
1. Are you <u>happy</u> about this decision?	
2. Does your supervisor <u>agree</u>?	
3. What if you <u>spoke</u> with her <u>directly</u>?	
4. Do you learn from <u>books or by talking to people</u>?	
5. <u>Have you thought about firing</u> him?	
6. Could you have <u>a weekly meeting</u> with them?	
7. Would <u>Tuesday</u> be a good time to talk?	
8. <u>Are</u> you living out your vision?	
9. Does your spouse think the <u>same way</u>?	
10. Are you going to <u>ask</u> him?	
11. Is the economy <u>killing</u> your budget?	
12. Could someone <u>on your team</u> help?	
13. Did you <u>reach</u> your annual goals yet?	
14. Did you have a <u>nice day</u> at school?	
15. Is <u>teaching</u> your main thing?	
16. Is <u>casting vision</u> the next step for the team?	

Types of Questions

1. Closed Questions

Questions that can be answered yes or no.

Do you agree with this approach?

Is it okay if we move on to another topic?

Are you ready to discuss this?

2. Open Questions

Questions that cannot be answered yes or no. Open questions require coachees to reflect and to express their thoughts verbally.

What is happening in your work right now?

What is the Lord saying to you about this decision?

When are you thinking of making a change?

3. Emotions Questions

Notice, acknowledge, and explore emotions. Understanding feelings can give the coachee insights into their behaviors, motivations, and plans.

What emotions are you experiencing as you enter this new phase of your life?

What's behind those tears?

Where is that [*fill in what you're noticing*] **coming from?**

4. Facts Questions

Gather the facts with questions like Who, What, When, Where, etc. Be careful not to interrogate!

Who is on the team?

What happened?

When did that happen?

Where did you go next?

5. Why Questions

The question "Why" is difficult to answer because it may force judgments that are premature to the conversation. It is also backward-looking, while we want to be forward-looking. Use other question words and prompt for multiple answers.

What factors are causing you to stop?

How would you summarize the results of your project?

What motivations do you have for achieving this?

6. Permission Questions

This creates greater openness to your question by giving the coachee a choice before asking the question.

Do you mind if I ask you a personal question?

I'm noticing a pattern here, could I share it with you?

Pure Questions

Pure questions are questions that are neutral and come from a non-judgmental heart. Questions that are judgmental or negative tear down and disempower, rather than motivate and inspire.

In this exercise you will change negative and judgmental questions or statements into non-judgmental or neutral inquiry.

Example 1

> **Judgmental: What part does your negative attitude play in this problem?**
>
> **Neutral: How might your mindset be helping or hindering this situation?**

The coach viewed the coachee's attitude as negative, however, the coachee may become defensive. A neutral question may promote discovery in the coachee.

Example 2

> **Negative: Have you thought about firing him?**
>
> **Neutral: What options do you see in working with him?**

Suggesting dismissal through a question directs the coachee to that option. The second question is positive and hopeful, encouraging the coachee to seek further options and not give up.

Instructions

Rewrite the following questions or statements to be non-judgmental or neutral inquiry.

1. What don't you like about your current position?

2. What's wrong with this organization?

_____

_____

3. That will never work.

_____

_____

4. How could you be less of a dictator in your leadership style?

_____

_____

5. That's a stupid idea.

_____

_____

6. I don't think your current approach is working, what would you like to try next?

_____

_____

7. How could you be more of a team player in this situation?

_____

_____

Q360

Asking questions from many different angles can help broaden the coachee's perspective and increase insights. Begin with a summary, followed by a question from the new angle.

Start here ↘

Background
- Explain the situation.
- Step back for a moment, what are the underlying issues?

Result
- What result would you like to have from this situation?
- What would achieving that do for you?

Interpersonal
- What are the relational dynamics in this situation?
- What relational work needs to be done to move forward?

Spiritual
- From a spiritual perspective, what do you see?
- What spiritual solutions might be helpful?

Values
- Which of your values are you trying to honor in this situation?
- How might you do that?

Cultural
- In what ways might culture be involved?
- What are normal cultural ways of handling this?

Inner Change
- What changes need to be made in you?
- How would you describe yourself with the changes in effect?

Systemic
- What other factors are influencing this situation?
- How can you use these factors to move forward?

End here ↘

Strategy
- What are the first steps to work on this?
- What parts give you energy?

Generating Feedback

Instead, speaking the truth in love, we will grow to become in every respect the mature body of him who is the head, that is, Christ.

—Ephesians 4:15

People may want help, but they don't want to be fixed.

—Keith Webb

Generating high-quality relevant feedback, as far as possible from within rather than from experts, is essential for continuous improvement, at work, in sport and in all aspects of life.

—John Whitmore

We judge ourselves by what we feel capable of doing, while others judge us by what we have already done.

—Henry Wadsworth Longfellow

Reinforcement

Reinforce all forward movement, without labeling it as "good" or "bad".

I acknowledge …

I recognize …

I noticed you …

You …

Exercise

Blind Spots

The human eye has a built-in blind spot, a place that it cannot see.

Right Eye

Cover your left eye and focus on the dot with your right eye.

Left Eye

Cover your right eye and focus on the dot with your left eye.

Your blind spot is the place where all the eye nerves gather and leave the eyeball for the brain. If you look straight ahead through your right eye your blind spot is at 4 o'clock, or 7 o'clock with your left eye. Yet, we don't see our blind spots. Our brain fills in the missing visual information.

How do blind spots affect your perceptions in coaching? How can you coach in such a way as to overcome your and the coachee's blind spots?

How to Generate Feedback

The goal of feedback is to provide useful information to help a person improve and develop. This information can reinforce positive behaviors or point out blind spots the person wasn't aware of. While giving feedback involves telling your observations to another person, you can generate feedback in the coachee through powerful questions.

> Generating high-quality relevant feedback, as far as possible from within rather than from experts, is essential for continuous improvement, at work, in sport and in all aspects of life.
>
> —John Whitmore

Have the Coachee Self-Evaluate

Generate feedback by asking the coachee to self-evaluate for a WIN! What they did <u>W</u>ell, could <u>I</u>mprove, and will do <u>N</u>ext time.

1. Ask about strengths. Affirm and ask for more!

    What did you do well?

    What else?

    I saw that too. I also noticed how you X and X and X.

2. Ask the coachee in what way they think they could improve.

    What could you improve?

3. Generate some possible future alternatives.

    How would you do that differently next time?

    What would you like to do next time?

Notes

Designing Actions

You see that his faith and his actions were working together, and his faith was made complete by what he did.

—James 2:22

Insights without action steps are just nice ideas.

—Keith Webb

We don't think ourselves into a new way of acting, we act ourselves into a new way of thinking.

—Bossidy, Charan & Burck.

Start by doing what's necessary; then do what's possible; and suddenly you are doing the impossible.

—Saint Francis of Assisi

Go For Small Wins

> It has long been an axiom of mine that the little things are infinitely the most important.
>
> —Sherlock Holmes

Small wins are critical for successful completion of a larger goal. Each action step is an opportunity for a small win. Results build on each other and compound into greater results, ultimately leading the coachee to accomplish their goal.

The Role of Small Wins

1. *Provide evidence that sacrifices are worth it:* Wins greatly help justify the short-term costs involved.

2. *Reward the coachee with a pat on the back:* After a lot of hard work, positive feedback builds morale and motivation.

3. *Help fine-tune vision and strategy:* Small wins give the coachee and coach concrete data on the viability of their ideas.

4. *Keep others on board:* Provides others with evidence that the goal is on track.

5. *Build momentum:* Progress toward the goal is established, others join.

—adapted from John Kotter, *Leading Change*

Action Steps

Insights without action steps are just good ideas. Action steps are the transitions from thoughts and ideas to application into real life.

1. Single, identifiable actions.
2. Will move the coachee toward their goal.
3. Doable before the next coaching conversation.
4. Can be thoughts, decisions, or actions.

Create 2 or 3 Action Steps Per Topic

It's essential that the coachee leave every coaching conversation having identified 2 or 3 action steps for each goal or topic they are receiving coaching on. It's assumed that all action steps will be completed prior to the next coaching conversation.

Example 1

Today's Coaching Conversation Goal: Figure out how to assess where our team is right now.
- I will read Kotter's book *Leading Change*.
- I will meet individually with Peter and Su-Jin to get their opinions of our current team dynamics.
- I will take Tuesday morning to pray and journal regarding next steps for our team.

Example 2

Today's Coaching Conversation Goal: How do I get started?
- I will find a gym and sign up.
- I will eat a salad 3 lunches this week.
- I will review my "stress list" every morning and pray through low score areas.

Example 3

Today's Coaching Conversation Goal: Do I need an MBA?
- I will use the Internet to research graduate schools with International MBAs.
- I will fine-tune my list of reasons I want to pursue an MBA.
- I will email my supervisor about using company time and money to do an MBA program.

Get SMART

Clear action steps or goals are like mini vision statements that describe a preferred future. Properly formed action steps motivate as well as form the basis on which to evaluate learning, growth, and performance. Coaches help coachees to create plans and action steps that are SMART:

Specific – clear, unambiguous

Measurable – you can measure or observe its completion

Attainable, yet a stretch – it's possible for you to complete

Relevant – it's meaningful to you

Time limited – when you will accomplish it

A Basic Pattern for SMART Action Steps

A SMART action step can be written following a basic pattern:

(Who) will **(what)** **(how much)** by **(when)**.
I will _____ by _____.

or

By **(when)**, **(who)** will **(what)** **(how much)**.
By _____ I will _____.

Who: Keep it personal, with "I" instead of an ambiguous "we" or "our team." Example, "I will spend at least 3 hours reflecting on my values and write a summary."

What: State what you will accomplish or complete. Watch out for "in process" statements like "I will try to…" or "I will work on…"

When: Include a deadline for when it will be completed, for example, "I will submit my article for publication within 10 days."

How Much: Include the degree to which it will be done, for example, "I will learn to speak Italian *to the point that I can order at a restaurant*."

SMARTen Up Action Steps

Below are examples of questions that you could use to coach a person to make their action steps SMARTer.

Specific: Action steps are written in a clear, unambiguous way as a finished result.

>   **Concretely, what does that look like?**
>
>   **What do you hope to achieve by doing this?**

Measurable: Action steps must be measurable or observable.

>   **How will you know when you've accomplished this action step?**
>
>   **How can you measure or observe that?**

Attainable, yet a Stretch: An action step that is realistic yet challenging.

>   **How challenging will this action step be for you?**
>
>   **What action step would move you not just a couple of steps ahead, but put you on a different level altogether?**

Relevant: Meaningful action steps increase the coachee's inner motivation.

>   **How important or meaningful is this action step to you?**
>
>   **How does this action step relate to your goal?**

Time-limited: Increases the likelihood that the coachee will accomplish it.

>   **What's your deadline for accomplishing this?**
>
>   **When do you plan to do this?**

Create SMART Action Steps

Use your own action step or choose one from below.

1. "I will try to control my email better."

2. "I will talk to my supervisor."

3. "I'm going to do personal development with my staff this week."

4. "I will spend time with my kids this week."

5. "I will pray about it."

6. "I think I'd like to think through my team's strategy."

Coaching Action Steps

Coaching actions steps is easy if the Awareness stage was done well. The coachee often already has ideas for action steps.

1. Ask for Action Steps

What actions could you take to move forward?

What else?

Prompt from different angles:

Who could help you?

What could you do differently in your preparation?

Earlier you mentioned X, is that something you'd like to do?

Which of these will you do?

2. SMARTen Them Up

Coach the action steps to become SMART.

Keep in mind, the Time Frame will often be the next coaching conversation.

3. Confirm

Confirm the action steps and make sure the coachee has written them down.

Which of these will you commit to doing?

How do you feel about these action steps? [Coach around any hesitations.]

Offering Suggestions

When integrating coaching skills into other roles, you may feel the need to give a suggestion. Hold off. If the other person has plenty of ideas, don't add your own. Keep asking for ideas – at least 3 times before offering yours.

1. Ask for other ideas.

What ideas do you have?

What else?

What else?

What's a crazy idea?

2. Ask for permission to share an idea.

I have an idea. May I share it?

3. Share it briefly, then right away ask,

What other ideas does that bring to mind?

Notes

Following Up

And let us consider how we may spur one another on toward love and good deeds, not giving up meeting together, as some are in the habit of doing, but encouraging one another—and all the more as you see the Day approaching.

—Hebrews 10:24-25

Reinforce all forward movement. Learn from both what worked and what didn't.

—Keith Webb

It is not difficult to know a thing; what is difficult is to know how to use what you know.

—Han Fei Tzu

When one door closes another door opens; but we often look so long and so regretfully upon the closed door that we do not see the ones which open for us.

— Alexander Graham Bell

Following Up Action Steps

Each coaching conversation you will ask the coachee a series of questions to follow up on their action steps. The purpose is to celebrate what was achieved – even if it wasn't the complete action step, explore what happened, discover and apply insights.

What? So What? Now What?

1. What?
Get a clear picture of what the coachee did regarding their action steps and what the results were. Dig a bit to expose the forward-moving thoughts and behaviors that can to be reinforced and acknowledged. Details help. Be generous with your acknowledgement.

> **What progress did you make on your action steps?**

> **What did you observe? Think about?**

> **What feelings did you have during the experience?**

2. So What?
Ask about the implications of doing this action step. Look for both content and process; content being the immediate results related to the action step itself, and process being the new thoughts, behaviors, and experiences involved in doing it. Look for insights and discoveries, especially regarding the process.

> **What benefits did you get from this experience?**

> **What did you learn? Relearn?**

> **How do you feel about the results? About yourself?**

3. Now What?
Help the coachee to extend the learning into other areas of his or her life.

> **How do you want to do things differently in the future?**

> **How can you extend the learning?**

> **Where else in your life could you apply that learning?**

Incomplete Action Steps

"Failure" is an emotionally charged word. Discouragement is its constant companion. Failure also has a note of finality or completeness. Black or white. Good or bad.

Every so-called failure is made up of several different actions – thoughts, decisions, or behaviors. While the overall result may not have been what was hoped for, some of the individual actions may have moved the coachee toward his or her goal.

Reinforce the forward movement before revising the action step.

1. What?

Identify the individual actions, not just the "failed" parts. Look for what they *did* do on the action step. What desired thoughts, decisions, and behaviors did the coachee do? Acknowledge them. Reinforce the desired actions, regardless of the final outcome. This will encourage the coachee, providing hope and motivation to press ahead.

> **What progress did you make on your action steps?**

> **You say it was a "disaster." What did you do first? How did that go?**

> **Then what did you do?**

Acknowledge forward-moving actions.

> **Yes, it didn't go how you expected. And yet, look at all the progress you made.**

> **You obviously put tremendous thought into that.**

> **I acknowledge your willingness to try. This wasn't easy.**

2. So What?

Explore the coachee's learning so far, before "fixing" the action step. This reinforces forward movement and sometimes reveals what went wrong in implementing the action step.

> **What do you make of your first few steps?**

What are you learning about yourself (or the situation)?

3. Now What?

In the case of incomplete action steps, do Now What? in two parts:

First, assess the coachee's continued commitment to it. Sometimes the action step is no longer relevant.

How important to you is it to complete this action step?

Second, if still relevant, coach the coachee through creating a plan to successfully complete the action step. This may involve modifying the action step, the timing, etc.

In what ways does the action step need to be changed?

Too big:

Would it be helpful to break the action step down into smaller steps?

Too Small:

How could you change the action step to move you further ahead?

Not in the Coachee's Control:

What part do you have the ability to personally complete? Where could you get help for the rest?

"Life" Got in the Way:

What needs to change for you to get this into your schedule?

Would you like to talk about the pressures you're experiencing in your schedule?

Worksheets & Highlights

Show me your ways, Lord, teach me your paths.

—Psalms 25:4

Reflecting and sharing with others cements our learning, rewiring our brains in the process.

—Keith Webb

When we are no longer able to change a situation we are challenged to change ourselves.

—Viktor Frankl

We had the experience but missed the meaning.

—T.S. Eliot

Personal Development Worksheet

Fill in your growth needs using the chart below. Focus on *your* desires for growth, not someone else's expectations for you. Don't worry if you don't know how you are going to achieve this growth. That will come later. First, identify in what ways you want to grow.

	Relational
1.	
2.	
3.	
4.	
5.	

	Professional / Career
1.	
2.	
3.	
4.	
5.	

	Leadership
1.	
2.	
3.	
4.	
5.	

	Intellectual
1.	
2.	
3.	
4.	
5.	

	Physical Health
1.	
2.	
3.	
4.	
5.	

	Spiritual
1.	
2.	
3.	
4.	
5.	

	Character
1.	
2.	
3.	
4.	
5.	

	Emotional
1.	
2.	
3.	
4.	
5.	

	Community Connection
1.	
2.	
3.	
4.	
5.	

	Hobbies / Recreation
1.	
2.	
3.	
4.	
5.	

	Marriage / Family
1.	
2.	
3.	
4.	
5.	

	Other Growth
1.	
2.	
3.	
4.	
5.	

Coaching Observation 1

Coach:_____   Observer:_____

Observe the coaching practice and use the self-evaluation questions to generate specific feedback from the coach.

1. What did you do well? (Affirm and ask for more!)

2. What could you improve?

3. How would you do that differently next time?

If there's time, ask about the following "angles":

Use of the COACH Model®

Listening skills (non-verbal, paraphrasing, clarifying questions, etc.)

Inquiry skills (number of questions, types, appropriateness, etc.)

What are three things <u>you as observer learned</u> from observing this coaching conversation? (This is for your own learning not to share with the coach.)

1.

2.

3.

Coaching Observation 2

Coach:_____   Observer:_____

Observe the coaching practice and use the self-evaluation questions to generate specific feedback from the coach.

1. What did you do well? (Affirm and ask for more!)

2. What could you improve?

3. How would you do that differently next time?

If there's time, ask about the following "angles":

Use of the COACH Model®

Listening skills (non-verbal, paraphrasing, clarifying questions, etc.)

Inquiry skills (number of questions, types, appropriateness, etc.)

What are three things <u>you as observer learned</u> from observing this coaching conversation? (This is for your own learning not to share with the coach.)

1.

2.

3.

Highlights

Reflect on all you've done today. What did you learn and how will you use it?

What useful insights or learning did you have today?

-
-
-
-
-
-

How will you implement your learning at the workplace or home?

-
-
-
-
-
-

Highlights

Reflect on all you've done today. What did you learn and how will you use it?

What useful insights or learning did you have today?

-
-
-
-
-
-

How will you implement your learning at the workplace or home?

-
-
-
-
-
-

Highlights

Reflect on all you've done today. What did you learn and how will you use it?

What useful insights or learning did you have today?

- ....
- ....
- ....
- ....
- ....
- ....

How will you implement your learning at the workplace or home?

- ....
- ....
- ....
- ....
- ....
- ....

Recommended Books on Coaching

Titles in **bold** are especially recommended.

Collins, Gary R. (2009). *Christian Coaching: Helping others turn potential into reality (2nd ed.).* Colorado Spring, CO: Navpress.

Horst, Tina Stoltzfus. (2017). *Dancing Between Cultures: Culturally intelligent coaching for missions and ministry.* Goshen, IN: Life Development Publishing.

McLean, Pamela. (2012). *The Completely Revised Handbook of Coaching: a developmental approach (2nd ed.)* San Francisco, CA: Jossey-Bass. Many of the psychological and sociological frameworks that inform our practice of coaching are included.

Ogne, Steve, & Tim Roehl. (2019). *TransforMissional Coaching: Empowering missional leaders in a changing ministry world.* Missional Challenge Publishing.

Stanier, Michael Bungay. (2016). The Coaching Habit: Say Less, Ask More & Change the Way You Lead Forever. Page Two.

Starr, Julie. (2011). *The Coaching Manual: The definitive guide to the process, principles and skills of personal coaching (3rd ed.).* London: Prentice Hall Business.

Stebbings, Kevin. (2018). *What Do You Really, Really Want?: Discovering What Matters Most And Taking Action To Achieve Your Important Goals.* Amazon.com. A novel following two coaching clients through a series of appointments. It's like watching 12 coaching demonstrations!

Stoltzfus, Tony. (2005). *Leadership Coaching: The Disciplines, Skills, and Heart of a Coach.* Privately published.

Webb, Keith E. (2019). *The COACH Model for Christian Leaders: Powerful Leadership Skills to Solve Problems, Reach Goals, and Develop Others.* Nashville, TN: Morgan James Publishing.

Webb, Keith E. (2015). *Coaching In Ministry: How Busy Church Leaders Can Multiply Their Impact.* Bellevue, WA: Active Results LLC.

Notes

About the Author

Dr. Keith E. Webb is a Professional Certified Coach, author, and speaker specializing in leadership development. He founded and leads Creative Results Management, a global training organization focused on equipping Christian leaders to multiply their impact. For 20 years, Keith lived in Japan, Indonesia, and Singapore where he designed and delivered leadership development programs. Keith created The COACH Model® and several International Coaching Federation-approved coaching training programs. He is the author of seven books, including *Coaching In Ministry*, *The COACH Model for Christian Leaders* and *Overcoming Spiritual Barriers in Japan*. Keith lives near Seattle and blogs at keithwebb.com.

COACH Model® Training

Now What?

Are you ready to take the next step in your coaching training? We teach and practice with you everything you need to coach effectively.

Learn the skills you need to multiply your impact!

Get On The Pro Track

Creative Results Management offers coaching courses fully online but "live" with Instructors and participants to build your coaching skills.

All of our coaching training has been examined and approved by the International Coaching Federation (ICF), the world's largest marketplace coaching association. In fact, you can go on to earn a professional coach credential.

⊘ACSTH
Approved Coach Specific Training Hours
International Coach Federation

Multiply Your Impact

Since 2005, Creative Results Management has equipped thousands of Christian leaders in practical leadership skills. We are one of the largest Christian training organizations focused on coaching. Visit our website today.

CREATIVE RESULTS MANAGEMENT

CreativeResultsManagement.com

Made in the USA
Monee, IL
27 June 2021